11+
15-MINUTE
PRACTICE PAPERS

Series editor Tracey Phelps,
the 11+ tutor with a

96% PASS RATE

Maths

English

Verbal Reasoning

Non-verbal Reasoning

Ages 9–10

Practice

SCHOLASTIC

Published in the UK by Scholastic Education, 2020

Book End, Range Road, Witney, Oxfordshire, OX29 0YD

A division of Scholastic Limited

London – New York – Toronto – Sydney – Auckland

Mexico City – New Delhi – Hong Kong

SCHOLASTIC and associated logos are trademarks and/or
registered trademarks of Scholastic Inc.

www.scholastic.co.uk

1 2 3 4 5 6 7 8 9   0 1 2 3 4 5 6 7 8 9

British Library Cataloguing-in-Publication Data

A catalogue record for this book is available from the
British Library.

ISBN 978-1407-18374-9

Printed and bound by Ashford Colour Press
Papers used by Scholastic Limited are made from wood grown
in sustainable forests.

Author

Tracey Phelps

Editorial team

Rachel Morgan, Suzanne Holloway, Vicki Yates,
Sarah Davies, Julia Roberts, Jennie Clifford

Design team

Dipa Mistry, Andrea Lewis and Couper Street Type Co

Illustrations

Tracey Phelps

Contents

About the CEM Test

About the CEM test

The Centre for Evaluation and Monitoring (CEM) is one of the leading providers of the tests that grammar schools use in selecting students at 11+. The CEM test assesses a student's ability in Verbal Reasoning, Non-verbal Reasoning, English and Mathematics. Pupils typically take the CEM test at the start of Year 6.

Students answer multiple-choice questions and record their answers on a separate answer sheet. This answer sheet is then marked via OMR (Optical Mark Recognition) scanning technology.

The content and question type may vary slightly each year. The English and Verbal Reasoning components have included synonyms, antonyms, word associations, shuffled sentences, cloze (gap fill) passages and comprehension questions.

The Mathematics and Non-verbal Reasoning components span the Key Stage 2 Mathematics curriculum, with emphasis on **worded problems**. It is useful to note that the CEM test does include mathematics topics introduced at Year 6, such as ratio, proportion and probability.

The other main provider of such tests is GL Assessment. The GLA test assesses the same subjects as the CEM test and uses a multiple-choice format.

About this book

Scholastic 11+ 15-Minute Practice Papers for the CEM Test Ages 9–10 offers authentic multiple-choice papers covering all of the key 11+ skills identified above.

This book contains:

- 13 15-minute practice papers, each containing 30 questions.

- Multiple-choice questions that reflect the different question types that are common in the CEM 11+ test, at a level appropriate for the age group.

- A coverage chart mapping the content of each test to the subjects and topics within the CEM 11+ test. Use this to identify areas of strength or weakness.

- Short answers are included at the end of the book. Extended answers are included at **www.scholastic.co.uk/pass-your-11-plus** or via the QR code below.

It is not expected that children will complete every timed test in the allotted time. Use the tests to develop test techniques and to gradually improve speed and accuracy as they get used to each question type. You might, though, wish to record how many questions your child is able to answer in each test and to work on increasing speed over time.

The following icons are used to allow you to identify the question types.

Shuffled sentences	Antonyms	Cloze	Pictures	Definitions
Comprehension	Synonyms	Maths	Word associations	Vocabulary

Practice Paper 1

 Space and the Human Body

Humans are not made for space travel. The microgravity environment of outer space causes several challenging health hazards.

One problem is swollen heads. Reduced gravity affects the water that makes up nearly two-thirds of our bodies. In space, fluids, including blood, rise up into the skull, puffing it up. Correspondingly, the legs
5 begin to deteriorate as they lose their normal amount of fluid. Bones lose density and weaken. "It kind of feels like you would feel if you hung upside down for a couple of minutes," explained astronaut Mark E. Kelly, an American space shuttle pilot between 2001 and 2010.

In addition, there can be vision issues. It seems that some astronauts' eyeballs flatten and, as a result, they become farsighted – they can't easily see things close-up. But the most serious issue is radiation. For
10 without the protection of our atmosphere, space travellers are exposed to harmful doses that increase their chances of getting cancer.

NASA scientists are working hard to solve the problems they are aware of. But there are always the unforeseen ones, those they call the 'unknown unknowns'. One unknown, for instance, is how additional time astronauts spend in space will affect the problems described above.

15 Time for solutions is short, for NASA's plan is to send astronauts to Mars within 20 years or so. Thus far, the longest anyone has spent in space is about 438 days. That record was set in 1994-5 by Valeri Polyakov, a Russian cosmonaut. It was only his second trip into space, to work on the Mir space station. The average time spent on space station missions is 2-3 months. But a return trip to Mars would probably take at least 3 years.

20 To investigate the effects of space travel on the human body, NASA conducted a lengthy study with the help of Mark Kelly and his identical twin brother, Scott Kelly, also an astronaut. While Scott went to space for a year, Mark stayed on Earth. Scientists conducted up to 10 tests a day, comparing the twins' initially identical bodies during this time. Their psychological wellbeing was also under scrutiny. One day, people will make the journey to Mars and it will be arduous in the extreme. The knowledge gained from NASA's
25 study on the astronaut twins will help travellers to prepare for the trials that will lie ahead.

Carefully read through the passage above and circle the correct answers below.

1 What percentage of the human body is made up of water?

A. approximately 30%   **C.** approximately 50%

B. approximately 2.5%   **D.** approximately 60%

---

2 Why do heads swell up in space?

A. Fluid collects in the head.   **C.** Bones lose their strength.

B. Astronauts hang upside down.   **D.** Nobody knows.

/2

3 Which of the following words is a synonym for 'deteriorate'?

A. ache

B. degenerate

C. swell

D. disintegrate

4 Which of the following health issues is not caused by reduced gravity?

A. weak limbs

B. swollen head

C. cancer

D. bones losing strength

5 What usually prevents people from being exposed to dangerous levels of radiation?

A. fluids

B. gravity

C. medication

D. the atmosphere

6 What is the longest time a person has spent in space?

A. 2 years

B. approximately 14 months

C. less than a year

D. 2.5 years

7 What does 'arduous in the extreme' tell us about what the first trip to Mars will be like?

A. an unplanned adventure

B. incredibly beautiful and relaxing

C. very physically and mentally challenging

D. a very uncomfortable experience

/5

The table below shows the price of single rail tickets from London to various towns.

Bristol	Bath	Oxford	Reading	Watford	Brighton
£88.75	£81.45	£68.55	£70.80	£54.75	£103.60

Write the answers in the boxes.

8 How much would two tickets from London to Bath cost in total?

Round your answer to the nearest £10.

£ ⬚⬚⬚

9 What would be the cost of a return ticket from London to Oxford?

Round your answers to the nearest £10.

£ ⬚⬚⬚

10 How much would the train fare be for four friends to travel from London to Brighton?

Round your answer to the nearest £10.

£ ⬚⬚⬚

11 What would be the cost of six single tickets to Watford?

Round your answer to the nearest £10.

£ ⬚⬚⬚

/4

 Circle the word which has the most opposite meaning to the word on the left.

12 courageous	fretful	careful	fearful	helpful
13 end	command	compose	commend	commence
14 precise	inaudible	inaccurate	inadequate	inappropriate
15 definitely	doubtfully	crucially	precisely	presently
16 formal	manual	casual	factual	punctual
17 shame	respect	disgrace	pride	courage
18 gentle	bitter	kindly	grim	harsh
19 weary	powerful	enterprising	energetic	exotic
20 allow	prevent	precede	prefer	presume

/9

Complete the sentences by circling the most appropriate word from the options A to E.

21 Ancient Egyptians believed that illness and disease was a _____ from the gods.

A	B	C	D	E
diagnosis	punishment	treatment	gift	reminder

22 There are living things that are so small they can only be seen through a _____ .

A	B	C	D	E
telescope	thermometer	microscope	stethoscope	barometer

23 The manufacture of textiles and clothing is one of the major _____ in China.

A	B	C	D	E
factories	industries	sports	studies	imports

24 Mountain climbing requires special _____ such as ropes to prevent falls.

A	B	C	D	E
guidance	skills	training	instructors	equipment

25 Pluto is called the _____ planet, as it is much smaller than the other planets.

A	B	C	D	E
red	inner	core	colossal	dwarf

/5

In each question below, the words may be rearranged to form a sentence. One word does not belong in the sentence. Circle the superfluous word from the options A to H.

26

scared	cats	of	Amy	and	is	pet	dogs
A	B	C	D	E	F	G	H

27

old	under	and	repairing	bridge	needed	was	the
A	B	C	D	E	F	G	H

28

in	hospitals	work	mainly	doctors	nurses	beds	and
A	B	C	D	E	F	G	H

29

milk	put	cereal	coffee	on	their	most	people
A	B	C	D	E	F	G	H

30

seats	quite	coaches	be	of	cramped	can	on
A	B	C	D	E	F	G	H

/5

Practice Paper 2

 In the following passages, some of the words are missing. Complete each passage by selecting the words from the options A to H. Each word may only be used once.

Passage 1

light	made	errand	luxury	steadily	opened	messenger	employed
A	B	C	D	E	F	G	H

Harrods is the world's largest department store and is located in the heart of London. The brand is synonymous with (Q1 _____) goods, in particular gourmet foods.

Charles Henry Harrod first (Q2 _____) his small shop in Knightsbridge in 1849. All his goods for sale were housed in a single room and he (Q3 _____) two assistants. He also employed a (Q4 _____) boy who would run errands for him and often make deliveries of tea and groceries to his customers.

From its humble beginnings, Harrod's became a fashionable place to be seen for London's wealthy shoppers and over the ensuing thirty years had (Q5 _____) grown into a large, bustling store.

Passage 2

installing	closed	display	rebuilt	children	soldiers	customers	profit
A	B	C	D	E	F	G	H

In 1883, a blazing fire engulfed Harrods department store and the building was razed to the ground. Undeterred, Charles Harrod took the opportunity to create an even more impressive store. With the help of eminent architect Charles Stephens, he (Q6 _____) his beloved store in a grand design, also (Q7 _____) the world's first escalator.

One of Charles Harrod's arch rivals was Harry Selfridge, whose eponymous store was also located in London's West End. Selfridge made a bet with Harrod over which of the two stores would make the most (Q8 _____) in the years from 1917 to 1927.

Harrods won easily and, as a gesture of goodwill, Harry Selfridge commissioned a miniature replica of the iconic Harrods building and presented it to Charles Harrod in a special ceremony that attracted a great deal of publicity for both brands. The replica is still on (Q9 _____) in Harrods to this day.

During World War II, Harrods contributed to the nation's war effort as it switched from selling luxury groceries to manufacturing uniforms for (Q10 _____) in the army.

/10

Tick the picture that is a 2D bird's-eye view of the 3D picture.

11

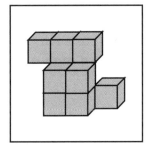   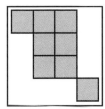   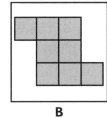   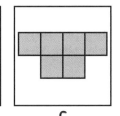   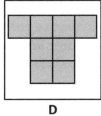

A   B   C   D

12

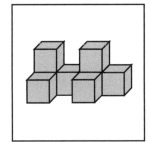   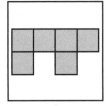   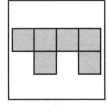   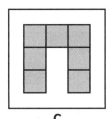   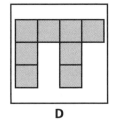

A   B   C   D

13

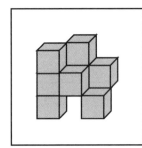   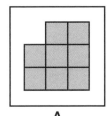   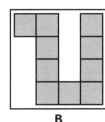   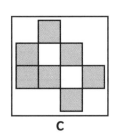   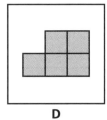

A   B   C   D

14

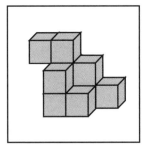   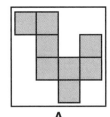   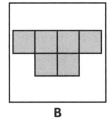   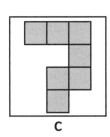   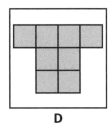

A   B   C   D

15

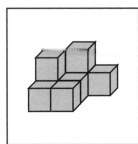   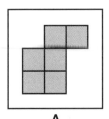   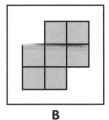   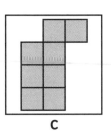   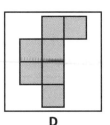

A   B   C   D

/5

In the following questions, circle the correct answer from the options A to E.

16 What is four-fifths as a decimal?

A	B	C	D	E
0.60	0.75	0.80	0.65	0.85

17 Which sum of money, when multiplied by nine, equals £126?

A	B	C	D	E
£12	£13	£14	£20	£15

18 How many days are there in 15 weeks?

A	B	C	D	E
105 days	110 days	112 days	118 days	120 days

19 What is the difference, in kilometres, between 34,280 metres and 12,170 metres?

A	B	C	D	E
2211km	22.11km	221.1km	2.221km	0.221km

20 If 420 × 150 = 63,000, what would 420 × 75 equal?

A	B	C	D	E
126,000	30,000	31,750	30,500	31,500

21 Round 6442.08 to the nearest 10.

A	B	C	D	E
6440	6400	6410	6450	6420

22 Which one of the following numbers is not a squared number?

A	B	C	D	E
16	225	144	64	27

/7

Match the words to the correct definitions. Write the correct answer A to J in the spaces.

23	remedy	
24	passport	
25	laboratory	
26	hermit	

A   a message that reminds someone to do something

B   someone who has chosen to live totally alone

C   a room containing items for use in scientific experiments

D   a person who is admired for having done something very brave

E   a card game for one player

F   a building from which books may be borrowed

G   a secret combination of letters used to log in to a device

H   an official booklet which proves your identity and allows you to travel abroad

I   a small village with just a cluster of houses

J   a cure for an illness

27	engrave	
28	separate	
29	hinder	
30	launch	

A   to give something your complete attention

B   to part or divide something

C   to choose a small number of things

D   to cut a design or letters into a metal or glass surface

E   to wash, dry and iron items of clothing

F   to start or introduce something fresh and new

G   to pay to use something for a short time

H   to make it difficult for someone to do something

I   to collect large numbers of items

J   to improve the quality of something

/8

Practice Paper 3

 Write the answer to each calculation in the boxes.

1 Ella has to take a spelling test at school.

There are 80 questions in the test and Ella gets 30% of her spellings wrong.

How many words does Ella manage to spell correctly?

2 Mr and Mrs Harding's daughter, Penny, is getting married and they are organising the food and drinks.

The Hardings decide that they will be serving sandwiches as part of a buffet lunch. The Hardings order a total of 240 sandwiches.

One-fifth of the sandwiches are going to be cheese and pickle.

How many sandwiches will be cheese and pickle?

3 Noor is reading a book which has 175 pages.

In one day she reads three-fifths of the book.

How many pages does Noor have left to read?

4 A car rental company has had some very poor sales figures and is having to sack one-eighth of its staff in order to save money.

If the company employs 24 people, how many of the staff will be able to keep their jobs?

/4

5 Olivia's mum is making pancakes. The recipe says to use one teaspoon of sugar to every three tablespoons of flour.

Sue uses three teaspoons of sugar in total to make a batch of pancakes.

How many tablespoons of flour did Olivia's mum use?

6 Tom goes to town on the bus.

There are already 9 passengers on board when Tom gets on the bus.

At the first stop 3 people get off and 11 people get on.

At the next stop 2 people get off and 9 people get on.

The next stop is the last and everybody leaves the bus.

How many people get off the bus?

7 Zahra has two sisters and she is the youngest. Zahra is seven.

Her eldest sister, Aylin, is twice her age.

Leyla is two years younger than Aylin and their mum is three times as old as Leyla.

How old is their mum?

8 Lucy owns 20 scarves in total. Four have green and blue stripes, five have pink and purple stripes, seven are plain blue and the rest are grey with blue spots.

How many scarves have the colour blue on them?

/4

Circle the word which has the most similar meaning to the word on the left.

9	windy	blistery	blustery	balmy	breathy
10	care	foresight	poise	caution	function
11	dangerous	chivalrous	perilous	disastrous	adventurous
12	separate	detach	deduct	reduce	remit
13	lift	elaborate	elongate	enlarge	elevate
14	show	announce	endorse	exhibit	promote
15	rapid	swift	scant	smart	stout
16	warm	aired	fluid	humid	tepid

/8

 Circle the word which you would most associate with the word on the left.

17	wharf	bicycle	boat	train	lorry
18	needle	connection	reflection	injection	inspection
19	playwright	theatre	hospital	museum	library
20	mind	coronation	imagination	destination	resignation
21	egg	struggle	tussle	scramble	shuffle
22	wheel	resolve	relapse	return	revolve
23	news	waiter	reporter	dentist	architect
24	mirror	retreat	react	reflect	reject

/8

Complete the passage by ticking the most appropriate word from the options.

Emmeline Pankhurst was born in 1858 to political activist parents. Her father supported the

anti-slavery movement; her mother was an

25
- [ ] advantage
- [ ] adversary
- [ ] advisor
- [ ] advocate

of women's suffrage. When

Emmeline started to go to women's suffrage meetings with her mother, she came to understand that

although women had to

26
- [ ] flout
- [ ] obey
- [ ] ignore
- [ ] influence

the law, they could not become law-makers themselves.

British law at that time

27
- [ ] deprived
- [ ] allocated
- [ ] approved
- [ ] proposed

women of any civil rights. Women, their earnings

and personal items all belonged

28
- [ ] illegally
- [ ] secretly
- [ ] legally
- [ ] loyally

to their father or husband. Girls had little

education; mothers had no rights over their children; and women were paid less than men. Women

couldn't

29
- [ ] speak
- [ ] read
- [ ] socialise
- [ ] vote

or become law-making politicians. So women couldn't end the injustice by

changing the law themselves. And, as they couldn't vote either, they couldn't even elect politicians

who did support women's rights. There was no legal way for them to

30
- [ ] charge
- [ ] vary
- [ ] adapt
- [ ] change

the situation.

/6

Practice Paper 4

 The *Orient Express*

In 1883, Georges Nagelmackers – a Belgian railway constructor – launched the *Orient Express* train service from Paris to Istanbul. His ambition was to operate the most luxurious train in Europe. It was the first continental train to feature dining and sleeping carriages. Many prominent journalists and businessmen were given complimentary tickets for the inaugural journey. They reported that they felt

5 like they were being transported in one of Europe's finest hotels, marvelling at the luxury leather seats, mahogany panelling and silk sheets on the beds.

By the turn of the 20th century, the *Orient Express* had become the most famous train in the world. Popular among European royalty, artists, businessmen and even spies, passengers enjoyed unrivalled luxury, fine wines, exquisite dining and opulent accommodation throughout the five-night journey through

10 the snowy Alps. The famous British crime writer Agatha Christie had long declared her love for the *Orient Express* and she finally achieved her dream of travelling solo on the iconic train in 1928. Christie subsequently often travelled on the luxury train and in 1929 – when returning from a visit to her spouse's archaeological dig – found herself stranded on the train for ten days when it became stuck in a snow blizzard 60 miles outside Istanbul. It is thought that while she was marooned aboard the train, she was

15 inspired to write one of her most successful mysteries – *Murder on the Orient Express.*

In the detective story, the book opens with a group of 14 passengers trapped in a carriage as the train is stopped in its tracks in a snowdrift just after midnight. Early the next morning, the body of millionaire businessman Samuel Ratchett is discovered in his compartment, stabbed a dozen times. Isolated by the storm and with a murderer in their midst, the Belgian detective Hercule Poirot must find the killer among

20 a dozen of the dead man's enemies, before the murderer decides to strike again...

Christie's book has since been made into several films which themselves have played their part in further glamorising the *Orient Express*, adding to its fine reputation and success. Nowadays, the train makes the trip from Paris to Istanbul just once a year and the iconic train journey is so popular that passengers must book several years in advance to be able to travel in such luxury through seven countries.

Carefully read through the passage above and circle the correct answers below.

1 What was the occupation of Agatha Christie's husband?

 A. He was an eminent surgeon.

 B. He was involved in spying for the British government.

 C. He was an archaeologist.

 D. He was an author.

---

2 What material was used for the panelling in the carriages on the *Orient Express*?

 A. They were made of wood.

 B. They were manufactured from steel.

 C. They were made of leather.

 D. They were made of brass.

/2

3 Which two on-board facilities was the *Orient Express* the first to offer its passengers?

A. En-suite bathrooms and the services of an on-board doctor in an emergency

B. A cocktail bar and air-conditioning throughout the train

C. Personal cabin attendants and complimentary champagne

D. Restaurant cars and cabins for passengers to sleep in

---

4 How often does the *Orient Express* now make the iconic journey from Paris to Istanbul?

A. Twice every year

B. Every month – departing on the first Friday of the month

C. Every week, leaving Paris at noon every Monday

D. Annually

---

5 Who accompanied Agatha Christie when she made her first journey on the *Orient Express*?

A. Her husband, Max

B. No one

C. Her publishing agent

D. Her father and one of her brothers

---

6 How did the murder victim in Agatha Christie's *Murder on the Orient Express* meet his death?

A. He was shot dead.

B. He was poisoned with strychnine.

C. He was stabbed.

D. He was pushed from the train as it was travelling at high speed.

---

7 Through how many countries does the *Orient Express* pass on its journey from Paris to Istanbul?

A. Seven

B. Five

C. Two

D. Six

/5

Recipe – Salmon with Sorrel Cream Sauce (Serves 4)

Ingredients

50ml milk
80g butter
50ml olive oil
4 x salmon fillets (skin on)
1 shallot
1 bunch sorrel
75ml white grape juice

200ml fish stock
200ml double cream
zest and juice of 1 lemon
300g new potatoes
300g purple sprouting broccoli
sea salt and freshly ground black pepper

Write the answer to each calculation in the boxes below.

8 If you were to make this recipe for eight people, how much double cream would be required? ◻◻◻ ml

9 If you were to make this recipe for six people, how much butter would you need? ◻◻◻ g

10 If you were to make this recipe for 12 people, how much white grape juice would you need to use? ◻◻◻ ml

11 If it was two people that you were catering for, how much fish stock would you be required to add? ◻◻◻ ml

/4

Circle the word which has the most opposite meaning to the word on the left.

12	**comedy**	remedy	tragedy	parody	melody
13	**trained**	uncoordinated	untried	awkward	unskilled
14	**irritate**	compose	soothe	quieten	diminish
15	**predictable**	stunning	sensational	surprising	smashing
16	**seldom**	chiefly	essentially	mainly	often
17	**correct**	unqualified	inaccurate	inefficient	unacceptable
18	**decline**	accept	accuse	incline	recline
19	**last**	official	menial	partial	initial
20	**permanent**	temporary	alternate	brief	fixed

/9

Complete the sentences by circling the most appropriate word from the options A to E.

21 A book and the human body both have an _____ and a spine.

A	B	C	D	E
index	foreword	appendix	heart	muscle

22 The word '_____' is the most commonly used noun in the English language.

A	B	C	D	E
on	the	be	she	time

23 The longest word in the English language containing no _____ is 'rhythms'.

A	B	C	D	E
synonyms	vowels	antonyms	consonants	homonyms

24 The words 'isle' and 'aisle' are _____ in exactly the same way.

A	B	C	D	E
published	pronounced	announced	produced	circulated

25 The phrase 'almost exactly' is a good example of an _____ .

A	B	C	D	E
oxymoron	simile	idiom	metaphor	tautology

/5

In each question below, the words may be rearranged to form a sentence. One word does not belong in the sentence. Circle the superfluous word from the options A to H.

26

patiently	every	for	Eva	over	hour	an	waited
A	B	C	D	E	F	G	H

27

a	handed	parcel	the	stamp	large	postman	me
A	B	C	D	E	F	G	H

28

see	the	could	only	I	fog	in	hardly
A	B	C	D	E	F	G	H

29

to	collected	raft	in	wood	build	they	a
A	B	C	D	E	F	G	H

30

lift	was	to	too	the	heavy	on	package
A	B	C	D	E	F	G	H

/5

Practice Paper 5

 In the following passages, some of the words are missing. Complete each passage by selecting the words from the options A to H. Each word may only be used once.

Passage 1

embarked	lengthy	cargo	sighted	crew	family	ambitious	timely
A	B	C	D	E	F	G	H

In early November 1872, the (Q1) ship Mary Celeste set sail from New York harbour to embark on an (Q2) four-thousand-mile voyage across the Atlantic Ocean to Genoa in Italy.

Benjamin Briggs was the ship's captain and, on this occasion, he was accompanied by his wife, Sarah and their two-year-old daughter, Sophia. The family took a (Q3) of seven sailors with them for the crossing.

A week later, the Dei Gratia cargo ship (Q4) on a similar crossing from New York.

In early December, the crew of the Dei Gratia (Q5) the Mary Celeste just off the Bay of Gibraltar; the ship appeared to be drifting.

Passage 2

left	extensive	fate	deserted	intact	thorough	shore	launched
A	B	C	D	E	F	G	H

Members of the Dei Gratia crew (Q6) a small boat and rowed over to the Mary Celeste. When they boarded the stricken ship, they discovered that although the vessel was perfectly seaworthy, the decks were (Q7) and there was no trace of the captain or his crew. All ten people had just apparently vanished without trace.

The Dei Gratia crew carried out an (Q8) search of the ship. It appeared that everyone on board had left the ship with great haste; the ship's cargo was (Q9) but the lifeboat and the navigation instruments were absent.

The Dei Gratia crew eventually sailed the abandoned Mary Celeste into port on the island of Gibraltar. The ship was examined by port officials but they failed to solve the mystery.

To this day, the (Q10) of Captain Briggs, his family, and crew remains unknown.

/10

Tick the picture which is the odd one out from the options A to E.

11

  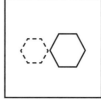

A   B   C   D   E

12

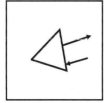 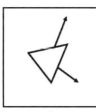   

A   B   C   D   E

13

 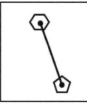 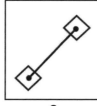  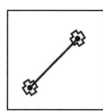

A   B   C   D   E

14

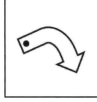    

A   B   C   D   E

15

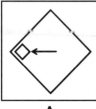  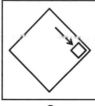 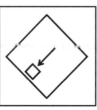 

A   B   C   D   E

/5

In the following questions, circle the correct answer from the options A to E.

16   If 25 May falls on a Tuesday, on which day of the week will 7 June fall?

A	B	C	D	E
Friday	Saturday	Thursday	Wednesday	Monday

17   Which one of the following numbers is the smallest number that is a multiple of 6 and 8?

A	B	C	D	E
48	96	12	56	24

18   How many seconds are there in five and a quarter minutes?

A	B	C	D	E
315	300	250	33	330

19   Which one of the following numbers is not a prime number?

A	B	C	D	E
7	23	29	15	11

20   Decrease £260 by 20%.

A	B	C	D	E
£52	£210	£198	£208	£220

21   What is the difference in grams between 13.7kg and 6.9kg?

A	B	C	D	E
0.68g	68g	6800g	6.8g	680g

22   What is 33 times 33?

A	B	C	D	E
1098	1034	99	999	1089

/7

Match the words to the correct definitions. Write the correct answer A to J in the spaces.

23	vital	
24	phenomenal	
25	constant	
26	flexible	

A able to change or bend

B very popular

C astonishing and amazing

D using different signs to represent different sounds

E helping poor people by giving them money

F essential and absolutely necessary

G easily influenced by people around you

H not different or special in any way

I happening all the time

J not necessary

27	garment	
28	creation	
29	technique	
30	narrative	

A a piece of elastic

B lack of knowledge

C an account about something that has happened

D a living thing

E something which has been made

F the answer to a problem

G a poem

H an item of clothing

I a storyteller

J a way of doing something

/8

Practice Paper 6

 Write the answer to each calculation in the boxes below.

1 Lucy, Zara and Arjun are all managing the cookie stall at the school fete and they have a total of 200 cookies to sell.

Lucy sells 67 cookies.

Zara sells 58 cookies.

Arjun sells 54 cookies.

How many cookies remain unsold?

2 There are 48 passengers on a double-decker bus.

Two-thirds of the passengers are seated upstairs.

How many passengers are seated downstairs on the bus?

3 Kiana has a bookcase where she keeps all her 125 books.

Each shelf has exactly the same number of books on it.

There are five shelves.

How many books are there on each shelf?

4 There are 44 tents on a campsite.

Thirty of the tents have three people camping in them and the remainder of the tents have four people camping in them.

How many campers are there at the campsite in total?

/4

5 There are 120 children in Year 4 at Tirley Primary School.

20% of the children walk to school and two-fifths cycle to school.

The remaining children travel by car.

How many children are driven to school?

☐☐

---

6 Henry wants to replace the tiles on his kitchen floor with new square tiles with sides measuring 1 metre.

His kitchen measures 3 metres wide and 5 metres long.

How many tiles will Henry need to buy?

☐☐

---

7 Dhanya is reading a book which has 192 pages.

She reads exactly 12 pages each day.

How many days will it take Dhanya to finish her book?

☐☐

---

8 Grace's cat eats three sachets of cat food every day.

When she goes on holiday for a fortnight, her neighbour agrees to feed her cat.

How many sachets of cat food will the neighbour need?

☐☐

/4

Circle the word which has the most similar meaning to the word on the left.

9	**predict**	forerun	forecast	forestall	forewarn
10	**rival**	candidate	nominee	representative	opponent
11	**extra**	additional	conditional	divisional	optional
12	**costly**	exaggerated	expendable	expensive	expansive
13	**beneficial**	pleasurable	practical	preferable	profitable
14	**seem**	emerge	appear	present	show
15	**appropriate**	correcting	balancing	setting	fitting
16	**mixed**	arranged	collected	assorted	opposite

/8

 Circle the word which you would most associate with the word on the left.

17	**pistol**	kindle	light	burn	fire
18	**stamp**	sentence	phrase	chapter	letter
19	**snow**	wander	drift	shift	stray
20	**valuables**	safe	neat	snug	sure
21	**lawyer**	library	bank	court	cinema
22	**witch**	write	spell	plan	draw
23	**shell**	snail	slug	spider	snake
24	**menu**	library	surgery	restaurant	pharmacy

/8

Complete the passage by ticking the most appropriate word from the options.

25
- [ ] scenery,
- [ ] history,
- [ ] beefeaters,
- [ ] land,

With almost a millennium of   the Tower of London has been, among

26
- [ ] discoveries,
- [ ] jewels,
- [ ] queens,
- [ ] things,

other   a prison and a place of execution. Anne Boleyn, the second wife

of Henry VIII, was charged with treason and beheaded at the Tower in 1536. Her ghost

27
- [ ] awkward
- [ ] wounded
- [ ] severed
- [ ] angry

has been sighted many times within the grounds of the Tower, with her

head tucked neatly under her right arm.

28
- [ ] neglected
- [ ] missing
- [ ] unwanted
- [ ] scruffy

Probably the most famous inhabitants of the Tower of London were the two

young princes, who were taken to the Tower by their uncle Richard. The boys were never

29
- [ ] onlookers
- [ ] librarians
- [ ] politicians
- [ ] historians

seen or heard of again. Many   are convinced that Richard ordered

30
- [ ] views
- [ ] stares
- [ ] looks
- [ ] sightings

that they be killed. Their true fate remains unknown but   of two young boys

in white gowns roaming around the grounds of the Tower have been reported for years.

/6

Practice Paper 7

 Marie Curie

Marie Sklodowska was the youngest of five children and was born on 7 November 1867 in Warsaw, Poland. She was clever and excelled at school and won many prizes and awards. At a very early age Marie became committed to the cause of Polish independence and was concerned at how Russian rule was making life very difficult, particularly for women, who mostly had no access to education. Marie had a
5   keen interest in chemistry, but there were no opportunities for her to study at the University of Warsaw, as they did not admit women, so she went to Paris in France to study at the Sorbonne. Marie earned a Master's degree in physics, chemistry and maths. It was in Paris that she met Pierre Curie, who at the time was in charge of the laboratory at the School of Physics and Chemistry. Pierre was a renowned chemist and they fell in love and married in July 1895. Marie studied radioactivity and in 1898
10   discovered two new scientific elements, radium and polonium, the second of which Curie named after her own country. Radium was found to have great powers and Marie and Pierre were able to study the science of radiation. The Curies' work proved that radiation enabled diseased cells in the human body to be burned away. In recognition of their ground-breaking research, the Curies were rightly awarded the Nobel Prize for Physics in 1903.

15   In April 1906, Pierre was tragically killed in a road accident, leaving Marie to raise their two children alone, and to manage the laboratory in Paris. In 1911, Marie was awarded a second Nobel Prize, in recognition for her services to the advancement of chemistry. Her work brought her success and fame but she also had to endure a lot of criticism and suspicion from a largely male-dominated world of science.

The onset of war in 1914 inspired Marie Curie to dedicate herself to installing X-ray machines in
20   hospitals; by the end of the war over a million soldiers had been examined by her X-ray units. It was an unfortunate side effect of her own ground-breaking studies and her prolonged exposure to radiation that led to her death from cancer on 4 July 1934. Marie Curie is remembered for her pioneering work in science, while at the same time elevating standards for female academic achievement.

Carefully read through the passage above and circle the correct answers below.

1   What was Marie committed to from an early age?

   A. Emigrating from her native Poland   **C.** Becoming a politician

   B. Poland gaining autonomy from Russia   **D.** Studying chemistry in Germany

---

2   How many years after her wedding day did Marie become a widow?

   A. 11 years

   B. 10 years

   C. 15 years

   D. 13 years

/2

3 How many siblings did Marie Curie have?

A. Five

B. Four

C. Three

D. Six

---

4 Which group of citizens was finding life especially challenging under Russian rule?

A. Trainee scientists

B. University lecturers

C. Women

D. Doctors

---

5 For which achievement was Marie Curie awarded a Nobel Prize in 1911?

A. For her discovery of radium

B. For her pioneering work in X-ray technology

C. For her discovery of polonium

D. For her services to the advancement of chemistry

---

6 When did Marie meet her spouse?

A. When Pierre was working as a teaching assistant in Warsaw

B. When she travelled to Russia for a job interview

C. When Pierre was managing a university laboratory

D. When Pierre was on holiday in Warsaw

---

7 What was the cause of Marie's death?

A. A fever she caught while visiting her family in Poland

B. Her continued exposure to radiation

C. A tragic car accident

D. Old age

/5

Write the answer to the each question in the boxes below.

The timetable below shows the times of the afternoon trains from London to Birmingham.

London (Euston)	14:03	14:13	14:49
Rugby	14:51	14:54	15:18
Birmingham Airport	16:02	16:04	16:47
Birmingham New Street	16:13	16:17	17:02

8 How many minutes does the 14:49 service take to travel from London to Rugby?

9 How many minutes does the slowest journey between Rugby and Birmingham airport take?

10 How many minutes does the quickest journey from Birmingham Airport to Birmingham New Street take?

11 How many minutes does the 14:13 service from London take to travel from Rugby to Birmingham New Street?

/4

 Circle the word which has the most opposite meaning to the word on the left.

12	verified	unconfirmed	unjustified	unreliable	unstable
13	glum	fretful	boastful	baleful	cheerful
14	sharp	short	blunt	rough	snappy
15	valuable	limitless	priceless	worthless	advantageous
16	betrayal	loyalty	fondness	treachery	duty
17	detain	apprehend	charge	collect	release
18	initial	late	final	extra	least
19	tolerant	abrupt	keen	impatient	sudden
20	expose	grant	allow	permit	mask

/9

Complete the sentences by circling the most appropriate word from the options A to E.

21 The Mughal Empire constructed some of South Asia's finest _____ .

A	B	C	D	E
mountains	memories	monuments	mementos	movements

22 The Romans were _____ road builders throughout the whole of Europe.

A	B	C	D	E
pilfering	patronising	profiteering	perishing	pioneering

23 Stonehenge is a collection of huge standing stones, _____ in a massive circle.

A	B	C	D	E
allocated	arranged	adapted	adjusted	anointed

24 The Ancient Greeks thought that the Earth was a flat _____ floating on water.

A	B	C	D	E
shrine	scrap	slice	slab	stripe

25 The Vikings were feared as they had a _____ for being bloodthirsty warriors.

A	B	C	D	E
character	opinion	reputation	popularity	prominence

/5

In each question below, the words may be rearranged to form a sentence. One word does not belong in the sentence. Circle the superfluous word from the options A to H.

26

tree	an	the	causing	wind	fallen	was	obstruction
A	B	C	D	E	F	G	H

27

prison	thief	crime	was	his	punished	the	for
A	B	C	D	E	F	G	H

28

a	film	very	ending	the	shortly	dramatic	had
A	B	C	D	E	F	G	H

29

only	confessed	sheepishly	breaking	the	to	window	Noah
A	B	C	D	E	F	G	H

30

were	in	candles	box	there	light	four	each
A	B	C	D	E	F	G	H

/5

Practice Paper 8

 In the following passages, some of the words are missing. Complete each passage by selecting the words from the options A to H. Each word may only be used once. Write the correct letter in each answer lozenge.

Passage 1

enthused	every	brightened	pretty	sighed	each	scene	fighting
A	**B**	**C**	**D**	**E**	**F**	**G**	**H**

"Christmas won't be Christmas without any presents," grumbled Jo, lying on the rug.

"It's so dreadful to be poor!" (Q1) Meg, looking down at her old dress.

"I don't think it's fair for some girls to have plenty of (Q2) things, and other

girls nothing at all," added little Amy, with an injured sniff.

"We've got Father and Mother and (Q3) other," said Beth contentedly, from

her corner.

The four young faces on which the firelight shone (Q4) at the cheerful words,

but darkened again as Jo said sadly, "We haven't got Father, and shall not have him for a

long time." She didn't say "perhaps never," but each silently added it, thinking of Father far

away, where the (Q5) was.

Passage 2

little	wanted	ought	giving	might	suffering	will	proposed
A	**B**	**C**	**D**	**E**	**F**	**G**	**H**

Nobody spoke for a minute; then Meg said in an altered tone,

"You know the reason Mother (Q6) not having any presents this Christmas was

because it is going to be a hard winter for everyone; and she thinks we (Q7)

not to spend money for pleasure, when our men are (Q8) so in the army. We

can't do much, but we can make our (Q9) sacrifices, and ought to do it gladly.

But I am afraid I don't," and Meg shook her head, as she thought regretfully of all the pretty

things she wanted.

"But I don't think the little we should spend would do any good. We've each got a dollar, and the

army wouldn't be much helped by our (Q10) that."

Extract from *Little Women* by Louisa May Alcott

/10

Tick the picture that best completes the set on the left from the options A to E.

11

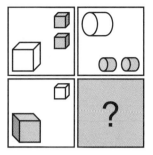

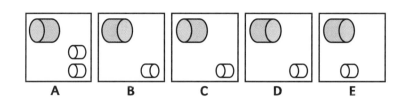

A   B   C   D   E

12

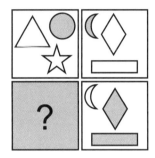

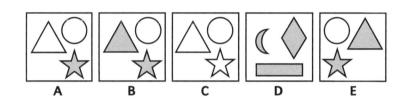

A   B   C   D   E

13

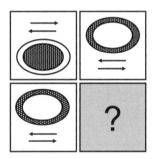

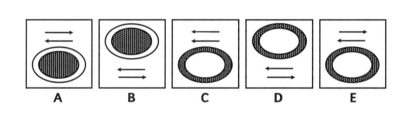

A   B   C   D   E

14

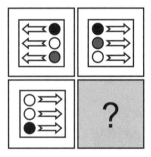

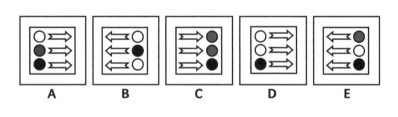

A   B   C   D   E

15

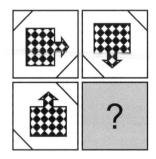

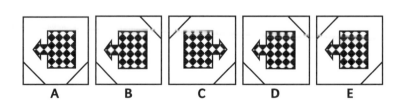

A   B   C   D   E

/5

In the following questions, circle the correct answer from the options A to E.

16 Which of the following numbers has the closest value to 3?

A	B	C	D	E
3.1	3.04	2.97	2.09	2.9

17 Which of these decimals is the same as $\frac{1}{5}$?

A	B	C	D	E
0.4	0.2	0.5	5.0	0.25

18 If 20% of a number is 35, what is the number?

A	B	C	D	E
105	120	135	125	175

19 If the temperature is 4°C, but falls by 9 degrees, what will the new temperature be?

A	B	C	D	E
–6°C	–5°C	–13°C	5°C	–15°C

20 What is the next number in the following sequence: 3, 5, 9, 17, 33 ?

A	B	C	D	E
65	62	72	82	96

21 How many hours are there in 4 days?

A	B	C	D	E
108	48	96	72	80

22 What is the time 42 minutes after 10.32am?

A	B	C	D	E
11.24am	11.04am	10.52am	11.12am	11.14am

/7

Match the words to the correct definitions. Write the correct answer A to J in the spaces.

23	hoard	
24	modify	
25	overlook	
26	banish	

A   to fail to notice something

B   to disappear

C   to alter something

D   to analyse something carefully

E   to hold or support something

F   to send someone away and not allow them to return

G   to repair or improve something

H   to continue to own something

I   to collect and store things

J   to make somebody less angry

27	novel	
28	standard	
29	handy	
30	inefficient	

A   neat and tidy

B   cheap and not of good quality

C   average or usual

D   not interesting or exciting

E   wasting time or energy

F   very amusing

G   easy to use and helpful

H   deserving sympathy

I   not having a plan

J   new and interesting

/8

Practice Paper 9

 Write the answer to each calculation in the boxes below.

1 Passengers are checking in for their flight to Madrid.

There are three check-in desks and each passenger is taking an average of two minutes to check in.

If the check-in desks all remain open for 40 minutes, how many passengers will there be on the flight?

2 Luis finds a recipe for king prawn risotto which says he needs 32 king prawns to serve four people.

How many king prawns will he need for nine people?

3 At the local police station 198 calls are answered between 08:30 and 10:00.

Of these calls, seven-ninths are emergencies.

How many calls are not urgent?

4 Samantha plants 260 bulbs in her garden.

She plants them in rows of 12 until she gets to the last row.

How many bulbs are in the final row?

/4

5 Kieran and Sienna have 240 books between them.

Sienna has 72 more books than Kieran.

How many books does Kieran have?

6 Lukas buys five dozen glasses for his birthday party.

10% of them get broken in the car on the journey home.

How many new glasses does Lukas have left?

7 Zala is going to cycle from Edinburgh to London for charity.

The total distance is 400 miles and Zala hopes to average 25 miles each day.

How many days will Zala's trip take?

8 160 children are on a school trip to Alton Towers.

$\frac{1}{8}$ of the children took egg sandwiches for their lunch and half took tuna sandwiches.

The rest of the children took cheese sandwiches.

How many children took cheese sandwiches?

/4

Circle the word which has the most similar meaning to the word on the left.

9	loathe	detest	decode	defer	demand
10	increase	endow	engulf	enlarge	endorse
11	above	within	beyond	before	overhead
12	jealous	devious	envious	ominous	callous
13	freedom	loyalty	amnesty	liberty	penalty
14	believable	gullible	illegible	implausible	credible
15	likely	probable	apparent	reasonable	impartial
16	change	moderate	alter	improve	inspect

/8

 Circle the word which you would most associate with the word on the left.

17	cobweb	scorpion	spider	snake	sloth
18	firework	expire	export	explode	explore
19	beach	bubbly	knobbly	pebbly	crumbly
20	airport	archway	runway	hallway	gateway
21	acorn	beech	pine	yew	oak
22	bandage	florist	tailor	nurse	secretary
23	unicorn	mythical	physical	tropical	chemical
24	fungus	mackerel	mango	mushroom	melon

/8

Complete the passage by ticking the most appropriate word from the options.

25 ☐ projects
☐ prospects
☐ promises
☐ proposals

Prior to World War I breaking out in 1914, women found that their career

were mostly limited to domestic service, working as servants in the houses of the wealthy.

26 ☐ joined
☐ endorsed
☐ prepared
☐ enlisted

But, as increasing numbers of men were   into the armed forces, women found

27 ☐ type
☐ area
☐ range
☐ scope

themselves called upon to replace men in a wide   of jobs. Almost a quarter of a

28 ☐ following
☐ further
☐ forward
☐ extra

million women were employed in government departments, while a   half a

million went to work in shops. One hundred thousand women joined the Land Army, working in

29 ☐ prepare
☐ produce
☐ provide
☐ protect

all areas of farming, including operating ploughs – large machines which   the

land for growing crops. By the end of the war, the gap between male and female wages had

30 ☐ interest
☐ allotment
☐ improvement
☐ contribution

narrowed and as a result of their   to the war effort some women were

given the right to vote.

/6

Practice Paper 10

 Cocos Island

Cocos Island is situated approximately 500 kilometres south-west of its nearest neighbour, Costa Rica. It is renowned for being the most famous treasure island in the world. The most well-known of the treasure legends is that of the 'Treasure of Lima'.

5 By the beginning of the 19th century, Lima, Peru's capital, had amassed a fabulous collection of valuable statues and jewellery in its cathedrals and churches. In 1820, many countries in South America were fighting for their independence from Spain and Portugal. The Spanish Army was fast approaching Lima and in response, Governor José de la Serna took the decision to have the treasures placed on a ship for safekeeping until the city was secure again. He opted for *Mary Dear*, captained by a very well-known and respected Scot named William Thompson. The governor instructed Thompson to steer his ship towards 10 Mexico and await further instructions when they arrived. However, the sheer value of his cargo was far too tempting for Thompson and his crew and instead they sailed to Cocos Island – in the Pacific Ocean – where they hastily buried the treasure. Shortly afterwards, they were apprehended by a Spanish warship. All of the crew, bar Thompson and his first mate, Forbes, were executed for piracy. The two men said they would show the Spaniards where they had hidden the treasure in return for their lives, and sailed 15 back to the island with the Spanish crew. Soon after landing on Cocos, Thompson and Forbes managed to escape from the Spaniards and after a few days, the British ship *Captain* arrived and docked at the island. Thompson convinced them that they were shipwrecked and stranded and *Captain* took them to safety to Puntarenas, in Costa Rica.

Within six months of arriving in Costa Rica, Forbes contracted yellow fever and died; and Thompson 20 went into hiding. Twenty years later, he happened to meet a man called John Keating and the two became firm friends. Thompson's health was declining rapidly by then, and on his deathbed he related the story of the theft to Keating and gave him a map and directions which he promised would lead him to the treasure trove.

Keating promptly sailed to Cocos Island to try to locate and collect the treasure but discovered nothing. 25 The 'Treasure of Lima' is believed to still be buried on Cocos Island to this day.

Carefully read through the passage above and circle the correct answers below.

1 Where is Costa Rica situated in relation to the island of Cocos?

   A. It lies to the south-west.   **C.** It is south-east of Cocos Island.

   B. It lies to the north-west of the island.   **D.** It is to the north-east of the island.

---

2 Where was William Thompson originally from?

   A. Spain   **C.** Scotland

   B. Portugal   **D.** Costa Rica

/2

3 In which ocean is Cocos Island to be found?

A. The Indian Ocean

B. The Pacific Ocean

C. The Southern Ocean

D. The Atlantic Ocean

---

4 Whereabouts in the city were most of Lima's treasures originally housed?

A. In the city's grand museums

B. At the governor's official residence

C. In the city's churches and cathedrals

D. In a set of secret underground caves beneath the city

---

5 What was Forbes's job on board *Mary Dear*?

A. He was the first mate.

B. He was the first officer.

C. He was the captain.

D. He was the ship's doctor.

---

6 How did Thompson and Forbes manage to avoid being executed for piracy?

A. They pretended to be Spanish.

B. They managed to escape.

C. They persuaded two other men from their crew to take their places.

D. They convinced the Spanish that they would divulge the location of the treasure.

---

7 In which year did William Thompson first encounter John Keating?

A. Around 1850

B. In about 1841

C. Around 1862

D. In about 1821

/5

Martha has a large hamper containing the following fruits:

Type of fruit	Number
Oranges	8
Bananas	3
Apples	6
Peaches	3
Plums	4

Please answer the questions in the boxes in the lowest terms.

8 Martha picks a piece of fruit from the hamper.

What is the probability that she picks out an apple?

☐ in ☐

9 What is the probability that Martha selects a plum?

☐ in ☐

10 What is the probability that Martha picks out an orange?

☐ in ☐

11 What is the probability that Martha selects a peach?

☐ in ☐

/4

Circle the word which has the most opposite meaning to the word on the left.

12	**tedious**	interesting	infuriating	devasting	stunning
13	**faulty**	fluctuating	engaging	functioning	focused
14	**juvenile**	mellow	manic	sensible	mature
15	**knowledge**	understanding	neglect	ignorance	tradition
16	**reveal**	concoct	condone	connect	conceal
17	**gather**	scamper	scuttle	scatter	scupper
18	**important**	trivial	tiresome	tricky	thrilling
19	**illegal**	lawful	artful	woeful	useful
20	**fuse**	determine	eliminate	separate	examine

/9

Complete the sentences by circling the most appropriate word from the options A to E.

21 Computers are now able to _____ the manner in which a human being thinks.

A	B	C	D	E
expect	judge	conclude	mimic	feature

22 In wet regions of the world, houses are often built on _____ to keep them dry.

A	B	C	D	E
guides	stilts	stalks	bunches	twigs

23 Conservation is the management and _____ of wildlife and its habitats.

A	B	C	D	E
protection	insurance	charity	destruction	threat

24 Scientists believe that the Earth is now too warm and that sea _____ are rising.

A	B	C	D	E
floors	layers	levels	stages	degrees

25 Sophisticated robots are now doing the work of _____ humans in factories.

A	B	C	D	E
powerful	cunning	alert	adaptable	skilled

/5

In each question below, the words may be rearranged to form a sentence. One word does not belong in the sentence. Circle the superfluous word from the options A to H

26

cancelled	day	compete	rain	due	sports	to	was
A	B	C	D	E	F	G	H

27

make	had	get	to	barely	time	we	dressed
A	B	C	D	E	F	G	H

28

faced	of	the	barrage	questions	a	crowd	politician
A	B	C	D	E	F	G	H

29

been	very	neighbour	fence	behaving	our	strangely	has
A	B	C	D	E	F	G	H

30

spent	tent	outdoors	we	camping	enjoyable	an	weekend
A	B	C	D	E	F	G	H

/5

Practice Paper 11

 In the following passages, some of the words are missing. Complete each passage by selecting the words from the options A to H. Each word may only be used once. Write the correct letter in each answer lozenge.

surely	scarlet	tries	wrote	often	lilac	knitted	mariners
A	B	C	D	E	F	G	H

Dora said it was all very well. She (Q1) says that. She was trying to mend a large hole in one of Noel's socks. He tore it on a nail when we were playing shipwrecked (Q2) on top of the shed the day Harry fell off and cut his chin: he still has the scar. Dora is the only one of us who ever (Q3) to mend anything. Alice tries to make things sometimes. Once she (Q4) a red scarf for Noel because his chest is delicate, but it was much wider at one end than the other, and he wouldn't wear it. So we used it as a flag, and it worked very well, because most of our things are black or grey since Mother died; and (Q5) was a very welcome change.

Extract from *The Story of the Treasure Seekers* by E Nesbit

already	bound	once	wheeling	waiting	travelling	anxious	reserved
A	B	C	D	E	F	G	H

It was a boiling hot day at the end of July, and the railway station at Tiverton Junction was crowded with passengers. Porters (Q6) enormous pieces of luggage were trying to force a way along the crowded platform while (Q7) mothers held restless children firmly by the hand. Harassed fathers sought to pack their families into (Q8) overflowing compartments and excited cyclists were endeavouring to disentangle their machines from piles of boxes. A circus and a theatrical company were complaining loudly that their (Q9) carriages were already occupied by other passengers, while a patient group of teachers were struggling to keep together a large party of boisterous children (Q10) for a sea-side residential trip.

Extract adapted from *Bosom Friends* by Angela Brazil

/10

Circle the picture that is a reflection of the picture on the left from the options A to D.

11

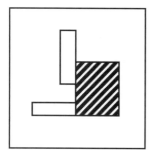  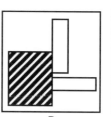  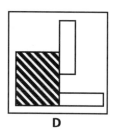

A   B   C   D

12

A   B   C   D

13

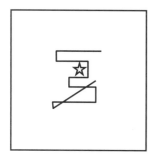 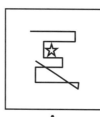 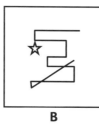  

A   B   C   D

14

A   B   C   D

15

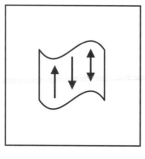 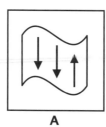 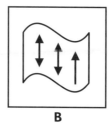 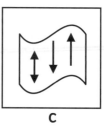 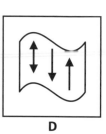

A   B   C   D

/5

In the following questions, circle the correct answer from the options A to E.

16 If two angles in a triangle measure 62° and 14°, what will the third angle measure?

A	B	C	D	E
114°	140°	104°	94°	96°

17 What is the area of a square with sides measuring 8cm?

A	B	C	D	E
48cm²	64cm²	78cm²	16cm²	32cm²

18 What is 20% of 110?

A	B	C	D	E
22	20	11	15	13

19 What is the total cost of three T-shirts costing £9.99 each?

A	B	C	D	E
£29.96	£21.99	£29.97	£29.95	£18.98

20 Which number is exactly halfway between 26 and 122?

A	B	C	D	E
70	72	73	74	84

21 What is two-thirds of 78 centilitres?

A	B	C	D	E
52cl	14cl	56cl	40cl	60cl

22 How many minutes are there between 12:35 and 14:15?

A	B	C	D	E
90 minutes	80 minutes	110 minutes	120 minutes	100 minutes

/7

Match the words to the correct definitions. Write the correct answer A to J in the spaces.

23	outcome	
24	centenary	
25	miniature	
26	option	

A   a smaller version of something larger

B   a period of 100 years

C   something that someone can choose to do

D   permission or agreement

E   the result of something

F   expenditure

G   a short piece of text describing a picture

H   the 100th anniversary of an important event

I   the smallest amount possible

J   a chance that something may be true

27	forlorn	
28	permanent	
29	rickety	
30	evident	

A   clear and obvious

B   direct and honest in behaviour

C   at an earlier time

D   weak and fragile and easily breakable

E   steadfast

F   lasting for a long time or forever

G   without violence

H   sad and lonely

I   having many small parts

J   unclear

/8

Practice Paper 12

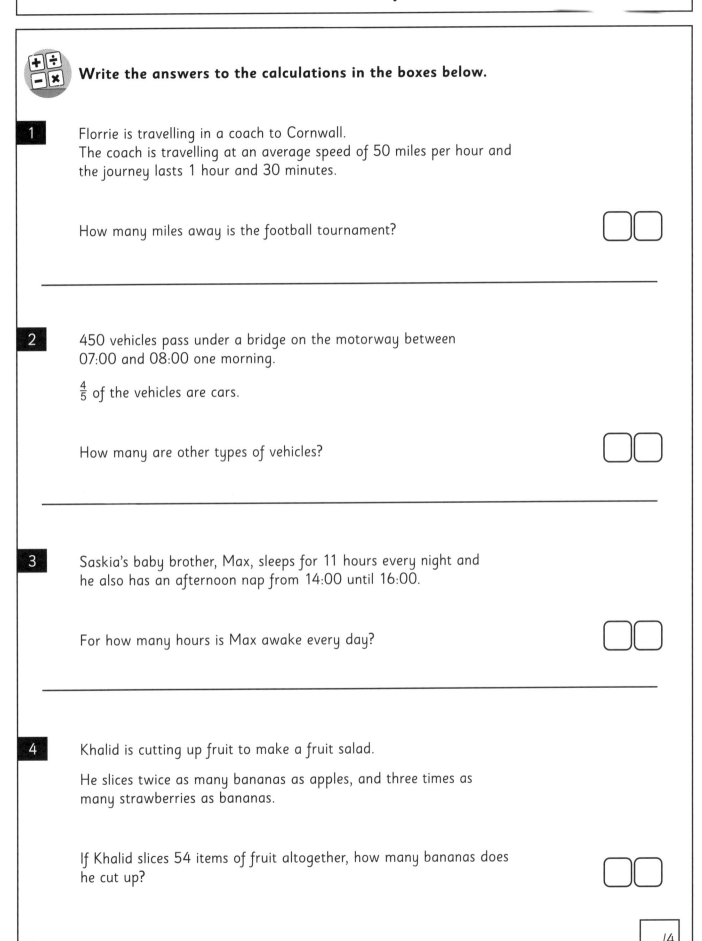

Write the answers to the calculations in the boxes below.

1 Florrie is travelling in a coach to Cornwall.
The coach is travelling at an average speed of 50 miles per hour and the journey lasts 1 hour and 30 minutes.

How many miles away is the football tournament?

2 450 vehicles pass under a bridge on the motorway between 07:00 and 08:00 one morning.

$\frac{4}{5}$ of the vehicles are cars.

How many are other types of vehicles?

3 Saskia's baby brother, Max, sleeps for 11 hours every night and he also has an afternoon nap from 14:00 until 16:00.

For how many hours is Max awake every day?

4 Khalid is cutting up fruit to make a fruit salad.

He slices twice as many bananas as apples, and three times as many strawberries as bananas.

If Khalid slices 54 items of fruit altogether, how many bananas does he cut up?

/4

5 In a tank there are 40 fish

In a second fish tank, there are twice as many fish as in the first tank.

In a third fish tank, there are 20% fewer fish than in the second tank.

How many fish are there in the third tank?

⬚⬚

---

6 A pet rescue centre is currently caring for 134 animals.

There are twice the number of dogs as cats.

There are 80 dogs.

The remainder are rabbits.

How many are rabbits?

⬚⬚

---

7 Maisie accidentally broke the television while playing a game.

Her parents insist that she pays half the cost of a replacement.

The new TV costs £400 and Maisie receives £5 each week as pocket money.

How many weeks will she have to save for?

⬚⬚

---

8 The whole school photo at St Mary's is to be on 6 September.

There will be a total of 225 people in the photo if everyone is at school that day.

One-fifth of the people in the photo will be teachers.

How many teachers does St Mary's have?

⬚⬚

/4

Circle the word which has the most similar meaning to the word on the left.

9	observer	spectator	speaker	saboteur	scrounger
10	sudden	aloof	adrift	adroit	abrupt
11	chore	timetable	errand	rota	routine
12	aged	fragile	feeble	elderly	miserly
13	tasty	appealing	appetising	attractive	admirable
14	advice	guidance	guarantee	assurance	knowledge
15	clap	appeal	appraise	applaud	appreciate
16	cunning	sprightly	swift	spirited	sly

/8

 Circle the word which you would most associate with the word on the left.

16	snake	autonomous	venomous	ravenous	eponymous
17	gem	scarlet	ruby	cerise	crimson
18	amphibian	tiger	turkey	toad	toucan
19	summit	mountain	river	lake	field
20	ship	pedal	rotor	saddle	mast
21	emerald	red	blue	green	yellow
22	inflate	cake	candle	balloon	hat
23	canine	horse	dog	cat	mouse

/8

Complete the passage by ticking the most appropriate word from the options.

The residents of Orkney are the most

25
- [ ] coincidental
- [ ] comparative
- [ ] contented
- [ ] convenient

people in Britain, according to a

recent survey. The jewel in the crown of the Scottish islands have been

26
- [ ] vetoed
- [ ] scored
- [ ] scaled
- [ ] voted

the best place to live in the UK. The islands came out on top, due to among other things,

high employment levels, low

27
- [ ] farming
- [ ] flying
- [ ] crime
- [ ] cycling

rates, inexpensive housing and excellent schools.

With its

28
- [ ] convincing
- [ ] realistic
- [ ] patterned
- [ ] picturesque

landscapes and a rich history dating back to Neolithic times, Orkney

is a popular destination for amateur treasure hunters and archaeologists hoping to unearth

valuable ancient

29
- [ ] artefacts.
- [ ] artists.
- [ ] archives.
- [ ] activists.

The majority of the islands' 20,000 permanent

residents earn their living working in the farming or fishing

30
- [ ] energies.
- [ ] industries.
- [ ] activities.
- [ ] factories.

/6

Practice Paper 13

 Job Vacancies

Trainee chef needed

Little Farms Restaurant needs a full-time trainee chef to start work immediately. You will be required to work five days, including weekends.

You will assist the head chef in preparing high-quality meals, in addition to cleaning and tidying the kitchen, designing menus and sourcing local, organic ingredients.

We are a small family business specialising in modern Italian cuisine. We offer a competitive salary and a full range of benefits, including twenty days' annual holiday, and opportunities for promotion.

You will have at least two years' experience in the catering business, preferably in a similar environment. Full training will be provided.

Bristol Zoo needs YOU!

The zoo is looking to recruit an assistant to work within our panda exhibit. The role will involve feeding and providing general care for our two adult giant pandas, keeping an eye on their health and cleaning out their enclosure. Additionally, you will be required to give talks to visitors twice daily.

If you possess an undergraduate degree in Zoology or Animal Biology, plus a passion for conservation, we would welcome your application. No experience is required. Applications are open until the end of the month. Please email your CV to recruitment@ bz.com.

Nursery teacher required

Appleford Primary School is looking for a qualified and experienced full-time teacher for our nursery class from September. We are a friendly village school with small year groups, and most of our children live in the local area. Responsibilities will include planning classroom activities, communicating with parents and supervising our two teaching assistants.

At least five years' experience in a similar role is required. We offer a competitive salary and a full range of benefits. This is a full-time position. For more details and to apply, please contact the school office.

Become a firefighter - The London Fire Brigade is now accepting applications.

To join the London Fire Brigade, you are not required to have any previous experience. You do need to be at least 18 years old and have GCSEs in English and Maths. The most important qualities you need to possess, besides excellent fitness levels, are discipline, a willingness to learn and the ability to keep calm in stressful situations. Becoming a firefighter is an extremely rewarding career, but it is not for everyone. To find out more, and to fill in an online application, please visit our website at www.lfb.org.uk

Carefully read through the text above and circle the correct answers below.

1 Which of the following statements is **true** about Little Farms Restaurant?

A. They specialise in traditional British cuisine.

B. They prefer to buy their ingredients from suppliers in their neighbourhood.

C. They are seeking a part-time trainee chef.

D. They run a farm and a restaurant.

/1

2 Which of the following statements is **true?**

 A. None of the positions explicitly require you to have a degree.

 B. The teaching position requires you to have the most experience.

 C. Only the catering position requires you to have experience.

 D. The fire brigade position requires you to have a first-aid certificate.

---

3 Which of the following is **not** one of the duties of the assistant at the panda exhibit?

 A. Checking on the animals' health

 B. Giving informative talks to visitors

 C. Cleaning out the panda enclosure

 D. Bathing the pandas

---

4 Based on the descriptions, which of the jobs require good communication skills?

 A. Firefighter and teacher

 B. Trainee chef

 C. Panda exhibit assistant and teacher

 D. Firefighter

---

5 Which of the jobs explicitly requires applicants to be good at keeping their composure?

 A. Firefighter

 B. Nursery teacher

 C. Trainee chef

 D. The position based at Bristol Zoo

---

6 Which of the following statements is **true?**

 A. The London Fire Brigade requires applicants to contact the website.

 B. Anyone with a passion for conservation can work at the Zoo.

 C. You need to be at least 21 years old to work as the trainee chef.

 D. The nursery teacher will have one teaching assistant.

---

7 Which of the following adjectives might best describe a career with the Fire Brigade?

 A. Fanciful

 B. Fortunate

 C. Fulfilling

 D. Fashionable

/5

Write the answers to the calculations in the boxes below.

8 Alex leaves Paris at 19:00 on a plane bound for Tokyo and the flight lasts for nine hours.

Tokyo is seven hours ahead of Paris.

What will the time be in Tokyo when he lands?

☐☐ : ☐☐

9 Sarah catches the 14:30 flight from London to New York.

Her journey time is 7.5 hours and New York is five hours behind London.

What is the time in New York when she arrives?

☐☐ : ☐☐

10 Mark flies from Singapore to Sydney – which is three hours ahead – on a three-hour flight.

He is due to leave Singapore at 15:00 but his flight is delayed by 30 minutes due to fog.

What is the time in Sydney when Mark eventually arrives?

☐☐ : ☐☐

11 Xi flies from Shanghai to London on a direct flight. London is seven hours behind Shanghai.

The flight takes 12 hours and he takes off at 00:30.

What is the time in London when Xi arrives?

☐☐ : ☐☐

/4

 Circle the word which has the most opposite meaning to the word on the left.

12	**compliment**	exercise	criticise	publicise	penalise
13	**rapid**	sullen	sluggish	churlish	stubborn
14	**assistance**	fragrance	endurance	hindrance	tolerance
15	**typical**	unnatural	classic	regular	unusual
16	**persuade**	deter	avoid	divert	avert
17	**condense**	exclude	exhale	expand	expire
18	**hazardous**	severe	serious	safe	sure
19	**thrive**	polish	punish	replenish	perish
20	**insolent**	polite	poised	polished	positive

/9

Complete the sentences by circling the most appropriate word from the options A to E.

21 Most of the world's supply of _____ metals originate from South Africa.

A	B	C	D	E
leading	bare	rusty	precious	advanced

22 Mineral water comes from natural _____ of water from beneath the ground.

A	B	C	D	E
fountains	jets	sprays	splashes	sources

23 A tornado is a very strong wind that twists and turns _____ to form a funnel.

A	B	C	D	E
gently	violently	amusingly	gracefully	valiantly

24 An _____ species is one where there are no more living examples on the planet.

A	B	C	D	E
endangered	extinct	exotic	rare	wild

25 Herbivorous animals eat plants, _____ carnivorous animals which eat meat.

A	B	C	D	E
dissimilar	contrary	unlike	opposite	different

/5

In each question below, the words may be rearranged to form a sentence. One word does not belong in the sentence. Circle the superfluous word from the options A to H.

26 patiently every for Ayesha over hour an waited

A	B	C	D	E	F	G	H

27 in her hospital Grandma went operation stayed after

A	B	C	D	E	F	G	H

28 an are complaint colds winter in a common

A	B	C	D	E	F	G	H

29 weather is picnic table it for ideal a

A	B	C	D	E	F	G	H

30 Jed a milk glass drank straw of half

A	B	C	D	E	F	G	H

/5

Answers

Practice Paper 1
p.5

1	D
2	A
3	B
4	C
5	D
6	B
7	C
8	£160
9	£140
10	£410
11	£330
12	fearful
13	commence
14	inaccurate
15	doubtfully
16	casual
17	pride
18	harsh
19	energetic
20	prevent
21	B
22	C
23	B
24	E
25	E
26	G
27	B
28	G
29	D
30	E

Practice Paper 2
p.9

1	D
2	F
3	H
4	G
5	E
6	D
7	A
8	H
9	C
10	F
11	C
12	A
13	D
14	B
15	A
16	C
17	C
18	A
19	B
20	E
21	A
22	E
23	J
24	H
25	C
26	B
27	D
28	B
29	H
30	F

Practice Paper 3
p.13

1	56
2	48
3	70
4	21
5	09
6	25
7	36
8	15
9	blustery
10	caution
11	perilous
12	detach
13	elevate
14	exhibit
15	swift
16	tepid
17	boat
18	injection
19	theatre
20	imagination
21	scramble
22	revolve
23	reporter
24	reflect
25	advocate
26	obey
27	deprived
28	legally
29	vote
30	change

Practice Paper 4
p.17

1	C
2	A
3	D
4	D
5	B
6	C
7	A
8	400ml
9	120g
10	225ml
11	100ml
12	tragedy
13	unskilled
14	soothe
15	surprising
16	often
17	inaccurate
18	accept
19	initial
20	temporary
21	C
22	E
23	B
24	B
25	A
26	B
27	E
28	D
29	D
30	G

Practice Paper 5
p.21

1	C
2	G
3	E
4	A
5	D
6	H
7	D
8	B
9	E
10	C
11	E
12	B
13	B
14	C
15	A
16	E
17	E
18	A
19	D
20	D
21	C
22	E
23	F
24	C
25	I
26	A
27	H
28	E
29	J
30	C

Answers

Practice Paper 6
p.25

1	21
2	16
3	25
4	146
5	48
6	15
7	16
8	42
9	forecast
10	opponent
11	additional
12	expensive
13	profitable
14	appear
15	fitting
16	assorted
17	fire
18	letter
19	drift
20	safe
21	court
22	spell
23	snail
24	restaurant
25	history
26	things
27	severed
28	missing
29	historians
30	sightings

Practice Paper 7
p.29

1	B
2	A
3	B
4	C
5	D
6	C
7	B
8	29 minutes
9	89 minutes
10	11 minutes
11	83 minutes
12	unconfirmed
13	cheerful
14	blunt
15	worthless
16	loyalty
17	release
18	final
19	impatient
20	mask
21	C
22	E
23	B
24	D
25	C
26	E
27	A
28	F
29	A
30	F

Practice Paper 8
p.33

1	E
2	D
3	F
4	C
5	H
6	H
7	C
8	F
9	A
10	D
11	D
12	B
13	A
14	B
15	E
16	C
17	B
18	E
19	B
20	A
21	C
22	E
23	I
24	C
25	A
26	F
27	J
28	C
29	G
30	E

Practice Paper 9
p.37

1	60
2	72
3	44
4	08
5	84
6	54
7	16
8	60
9	detest
10	enlarge
11	overhead
12	envious
13	liberty
14	credible
15	probable
16	alter
17	spider
18	explode
19	pebbly
20	runway
21	oak
22	nurse
23	mythical
24	mushroom
25	prospects
26	enlisted
27	range
28	further
29	prepare
30	contribution

Answers

Practice Paper 10
p.41

1	D
2	C
3	B
4	C
5	A
6	D
7	B
8	1 in 4
9	1 in 6
10	1 in 3
11	1 in 8
12	interesting
13	functioning
14	mature
15	ignorance
16	conceal
17	scatter
18	trivial
19	lawful
20	separate
21	D
22	B
23	A
24	C
25	E
26	C
27	A
28	G
29	D
30	B

Practice Paper 11
p.45

1	E
2	H
3	C
4	G
5	B
6	D
7	G
8	A
9	H
10	B
11	D
12	B
13	A
14	C
15	D
16	C
17	B
18	A
19	C
20	D
21	A
22	E
23	E
24	H
25	A
26	C
27	H
28	F
29	D
30	A

Practice Paper 12
p.49

1	75
2	90
3	11
4	12
5	64
6	14
7	40
8	45
9	spectator
10	abrupt
11	errand
12	elderly
13	appetising
14	guidance
15	applaud
16	sly
17	venomous
18	ruby
19	toad
20	mountain
21	mast
22	green
23	balloon
24	dog
25	contented
26	voted
27	crime
28	picturesque
29	artefacts
30	industries

Practice Paper 13
p.53

1	B
2	B
3	D
4	C
5	A
6	A
7	C
8	11:00
9	17:00
10	21:30
11	05:30
12	criticise
13	sluggish
14	hindrance
15	unusual
16	deter
17	expand
18	safe
19	perish
20	polite
21	D
22	E
23	B
24	B
25	C
26	B
27	E
28	A
29	D
30	F

Coverage Chart and Scores

	Practice Paper	Question number(s)	Page number(s)	Score
Comprehension	1	1 to 7	5 to 6	/7
	4	1 to 7	17 to 18	/7
	7	1 to 7	29 to 30	/7
	10	1 to 7	41 to 42	/7
	13	1 to 7	53 to 54	/7
Maths	1	8 to 11	7	/4
	2	16 to 22	11	/7
	3	1 to 8	13 to 14	/8
	4	8 to 11	19	/4
	5	16 to 22	23	/7
	6	1 to 8	25 to 26	/8
	7	8 to 11	31	/4
	8	16 to 22	35	/7
	9	1 to 8	37 to 38	/8
	10	8 to 11	43	/4
	11	16 to 22	47	/7
	12	1 to 8	49 to 50	/8
	13	8 to 11	55	/4
Antonyms	1	12 to 20	7	/9
	4	12 to 20	19	/9
	7	12 to 20	31	/9
	10	12 to 20	43	/9
	13	12 to 20	55	/9
Cloze	1	21 to 25	8	/5
	2	1 to 10	9	/10
	4	21 to 25	20	/5
	5	1 to 10	21	/10
	7	21 to 25	32	/5
	8	1 to 10	33	/10
	10	21 to 25	44	/5
	11	1 to 10	45	/10
	13	21 to 25	56	/5

Coverage Chart and Scores

	Practice Paper	Question number(s)	Page number(s)	Score
Shuffled sentences	1	26 to 30	8	/5
	4	26 to 30	20	/5
	7	26 to 30	32	/5
	10	26 to 30	44	/5
	13	26 to 30	56	/5
Pictures	2	11 to 15	10	/5
	5	11 to 15	22	/5
	8	11 to 15	34	/5
	11	11 to 15	46	/5
Definitions	2	23 to 30	12	/8
	5	23 to 30	24	/8
	8	23 to 30	36	/8
	11	23 to 30	48	/8
Synonyms	3	9 to 16	15	/8
	6	9 to 16	27	/8
	9	9 to 16	39	/8
	12	9 to 16	51	/8
Word associations	3	17 to 24	15	/8
	6	17 to 24	27	/8
Vocabulary	9	25 to 30	40	/6
	12	25 to 30	52	/6

Notes

Notes

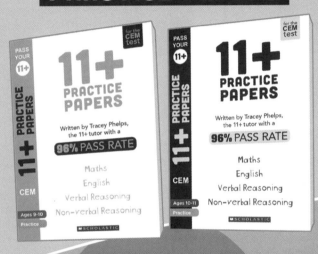